Fish and chips

Rocky and his mother wanted some fish and chips.

Here is some money.
Go and get some fish and chips.

1

Rocky went to the shop.
He bought some fish and chips.

When he left the shop he met Kevin.

Have you been for some chips?
Give me some!

2

3

There was only one left!

When Rocky came in, his mother picked it up.

Only one! Is that all?
What about the others?

4

Rocky went out.
His mother left the fish on the table.

A cat looked through the window.
The cat saw the fish.

The cat came through the window.

Lovely hot fish!

...but the cat picked up the fish and ran off with it.

Rocky went to see the men who made the chips.

Can I have some chips?

He bought chips, but no fish.

The other children saw Rocky.